VIOLIN SCALES AND ARPEGGIOS: GRADES 6-8

Edited and fingered by JACK STEADMAN

The examination requirements for scales and arpeggios given in this publication are applicable from 1985 onwards; but reference must always be made to the current syllabus, in case any changes have been made to the requirements.

Separate bowing (one note to a bow) should be played *simple détaché*. Slurred bowing should be played *legato,* with the whole bow wherever possible. A firm, sonorous tone should be used.

Scales and arpeggios should be played at a pace that is consistent with accuracy and distinctness, and without undue accentuation. The candidate should aim for a tempo that is compatible with a clean and firm tone, vital rhythm, controlled bowing and good intonation.

The fingering given in this publication is considered to be practical but it is not compulsory. Where two fingerings are indicated, that *above* the notes is usually for starting in the first position, with changes of position for the higher notes; that *below* the notes is usually for starting in a position other than the first, with an alternative fingering provided. Note that, when in the first position, either an open string or the fourth finger may be used.

THE ASSOCIATED BOARD OF
THE ROYAL SCHOOLS OF MUSIC

SCALE REQUIREMENTS & BOWING PATTERNS (Grades 6, 7 & 8)

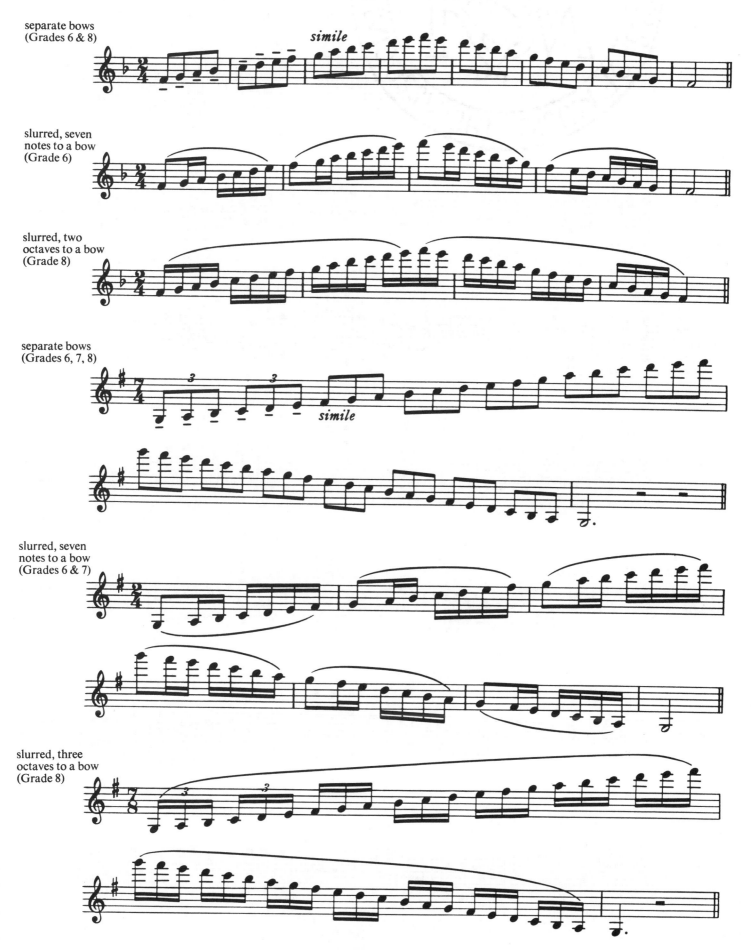

separate bows
(Grades 6 & 8)

slurred, seven
notes to a bow
(Grade 6)

slurred, two
octaves to a bow
(Grade 8)

separate bows
(Grades 6, 7, 8)

slurred, seven
notes to a bow
(Grades 6 & 7)

slurred, three
octaves to a bow
(Grade 8)

SCALES: 2 octaves (Grades 6 & 8)

(a) separate bows, even notes; (b) slurred, seven notes to a bow, as example on page 3 (Grade 6);
(c) slurred, two octaves to a bow, as example on page 3 (Grade 8)

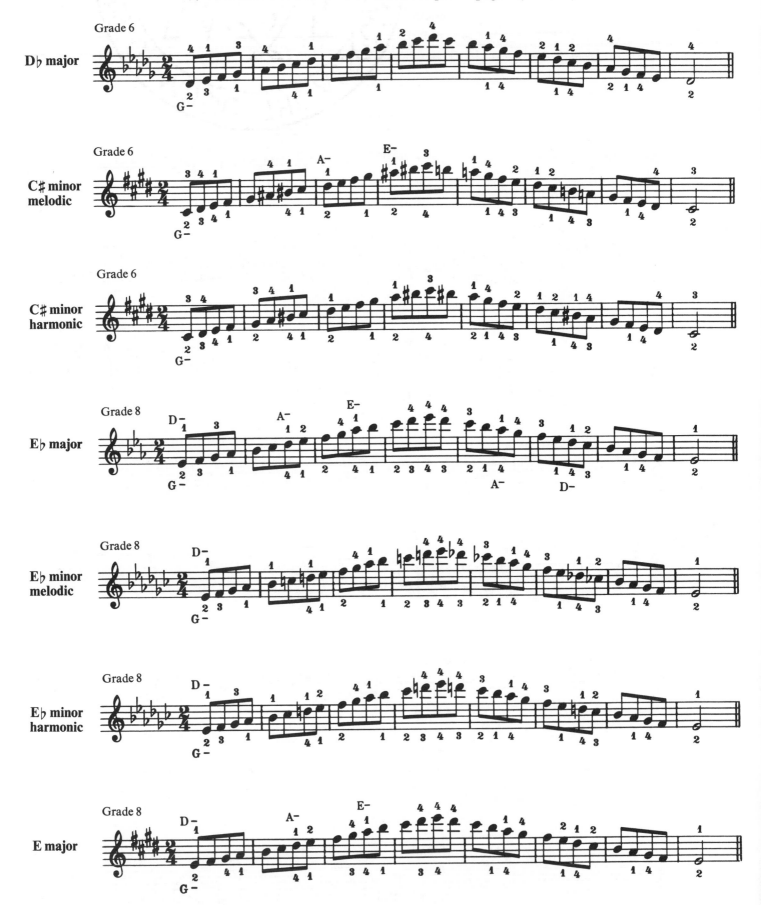

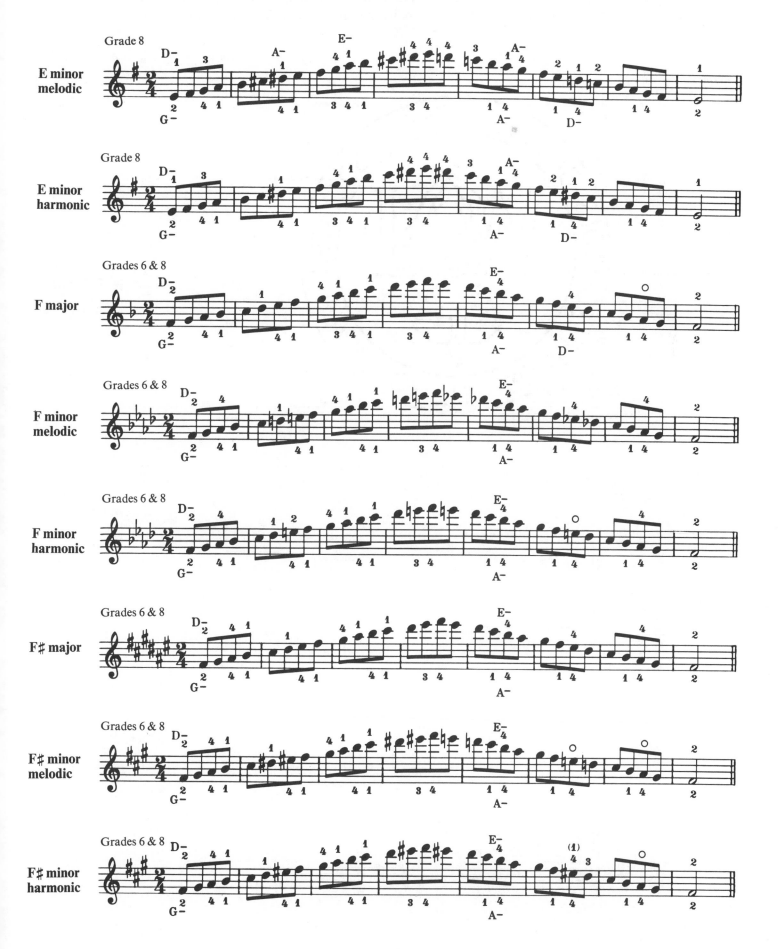

SCALES: 3 octaves (Grades 6, 7 & 8)

(a) separate bows, even notes; (b) slurred, seven notes to a bow, as example on page 3 (Grades 6 & 7); (c) slurred, three octaves to a bow, as example on page 3 (Grade 8)

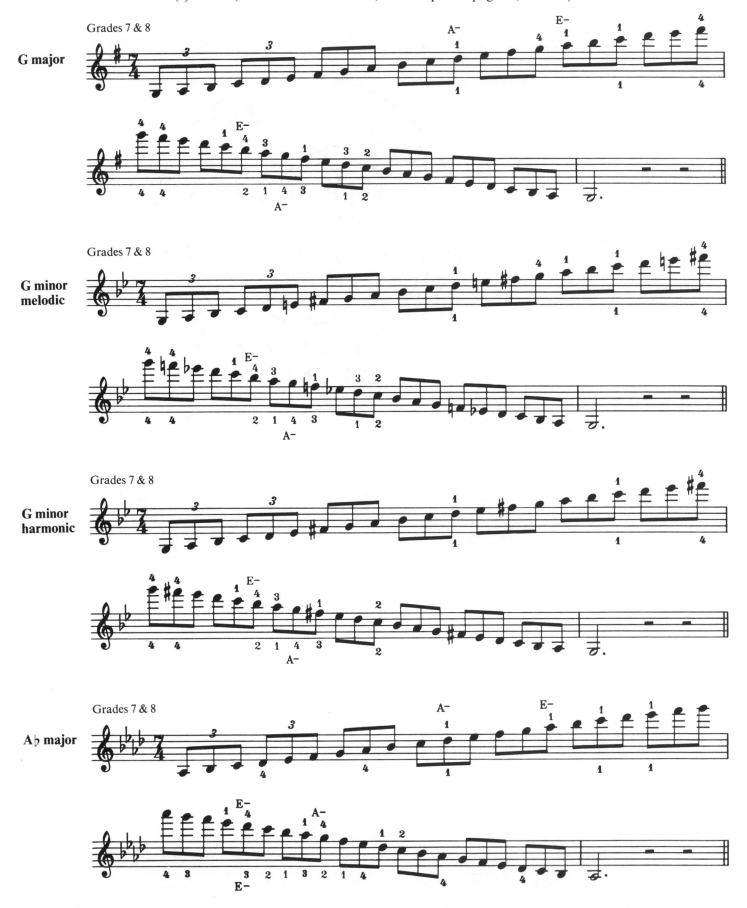

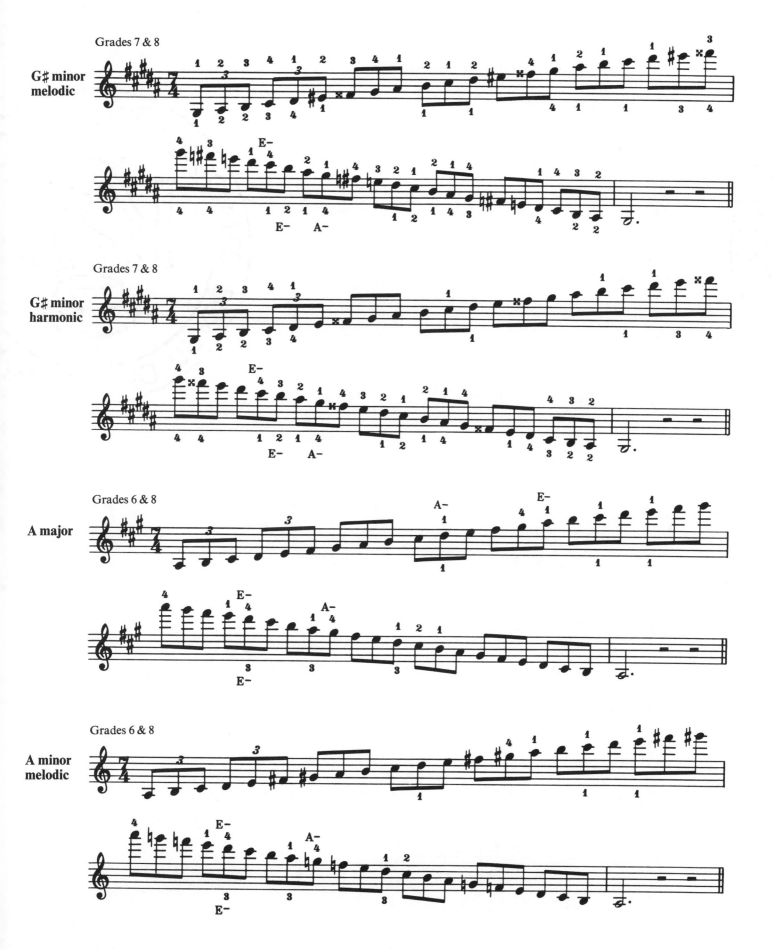

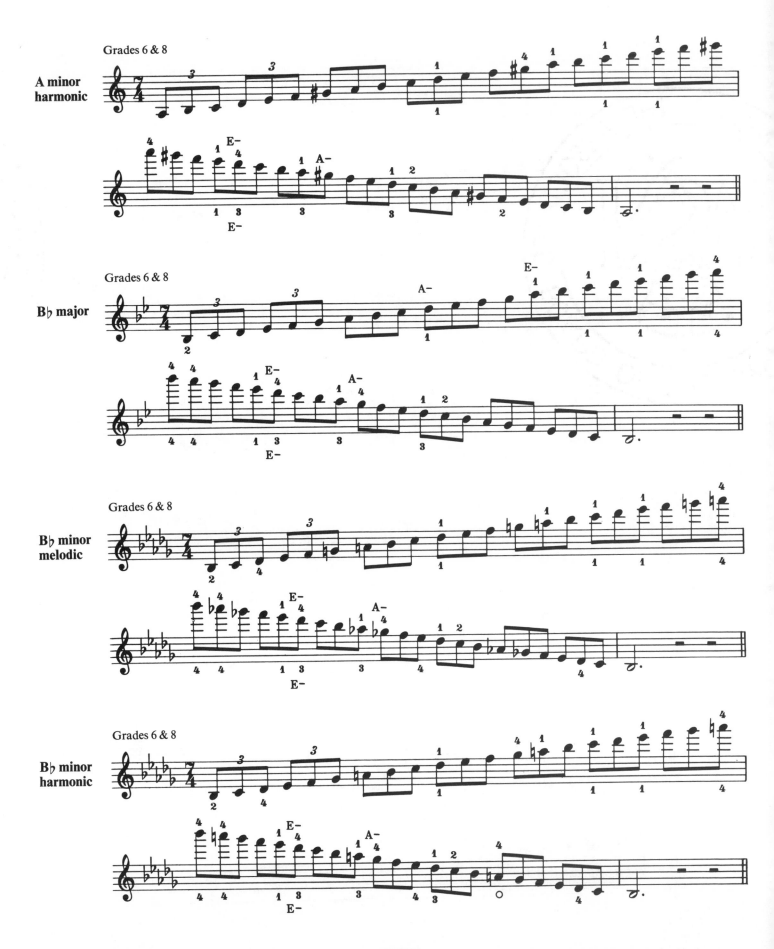

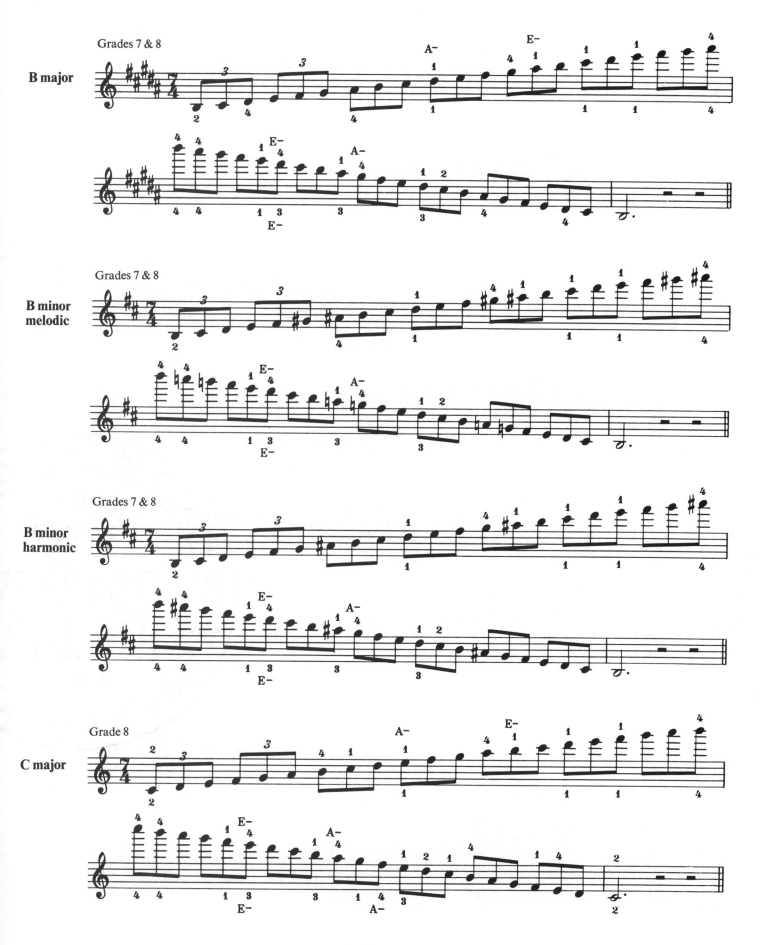

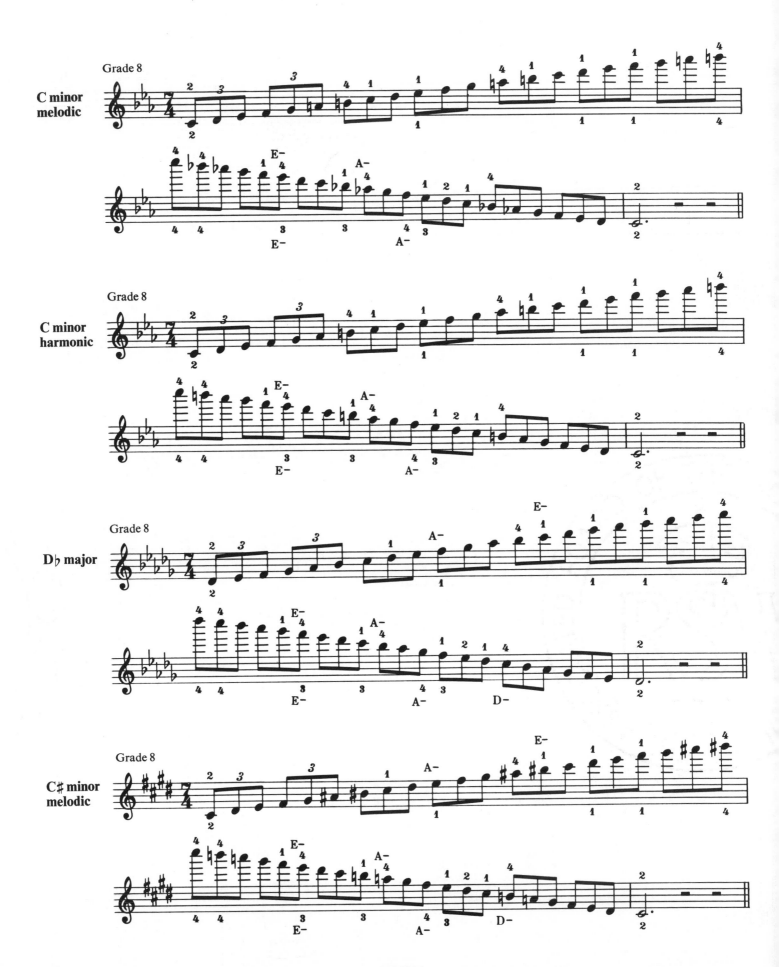

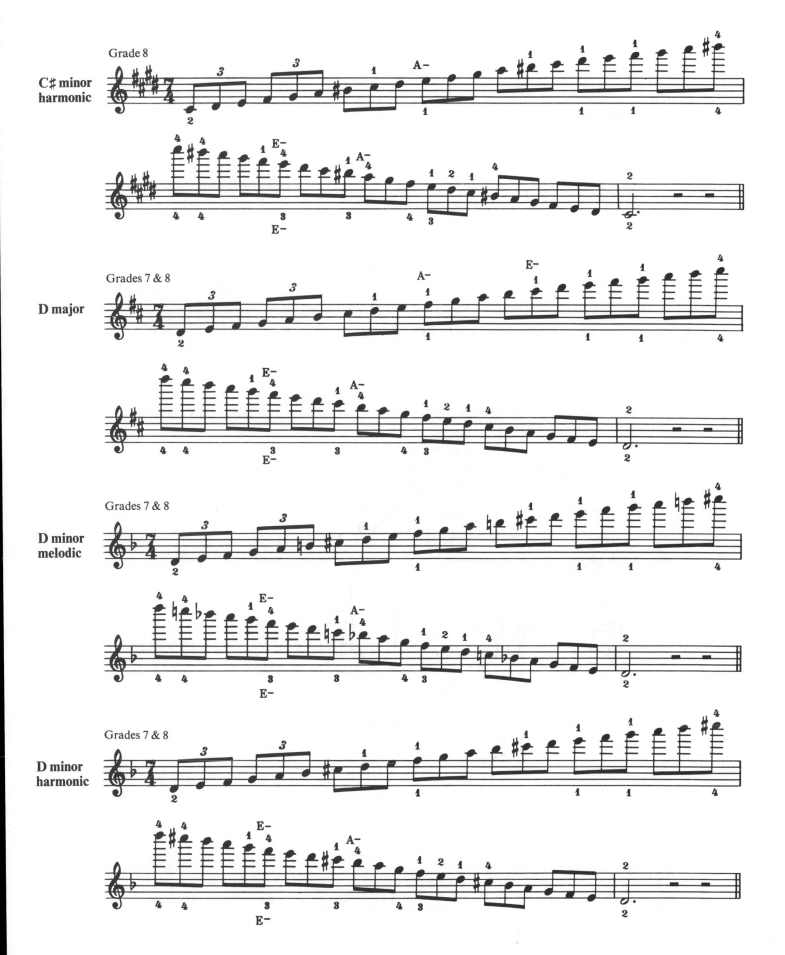

CHROMATIC SCALES: 2 octaves (Grade 6)

(a) separate bows, even notes; (b) slurred as shown, four *or* six notes to a bow at candidate's choice

CHROMATIC SCALES: 2 octaves (Grade 7)

(a) separate bows, even notes; (b) slurred as shown, twelve notes to a bow

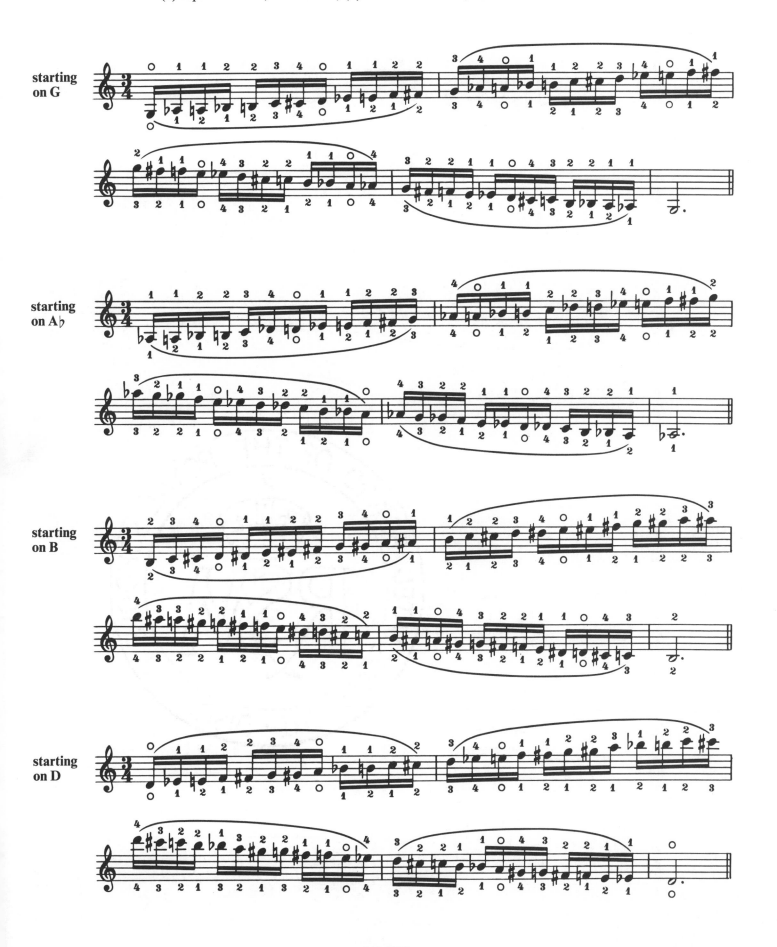

CHROMATIC SCALES: 2 octaves (Grade 8)

(a) separate bows, even notes; (b) slurred as shown, twelve notes to a bow

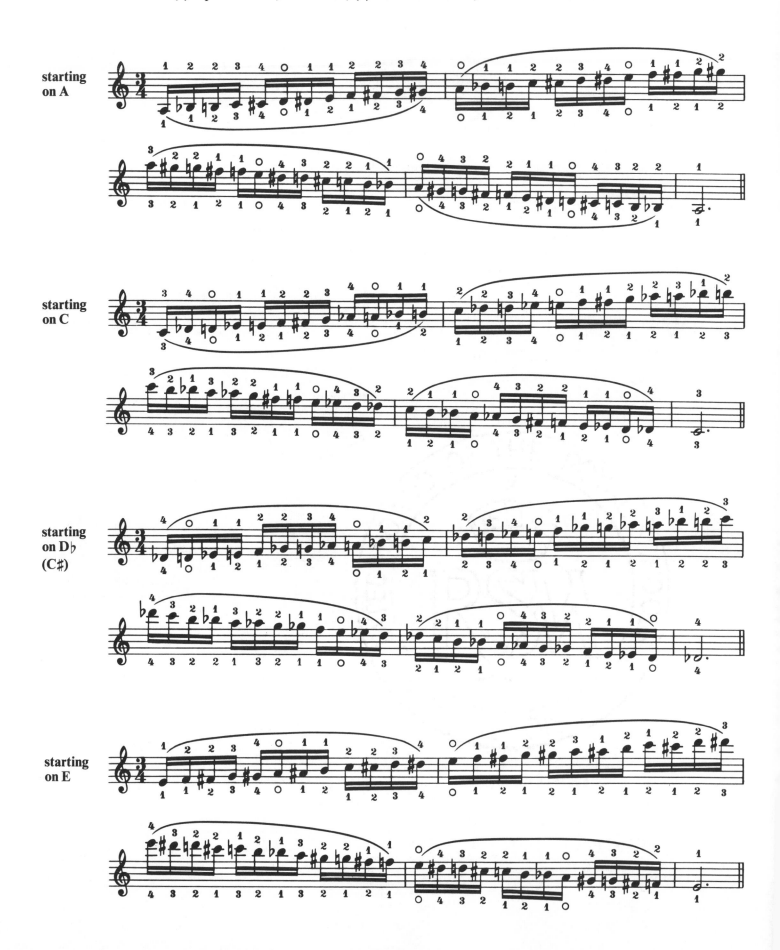

starting on A

starting on C

starting on D♭ (C♯)

starting on E

CHROMATIC SCALES : 2 & 3 octaves (Grade 8)

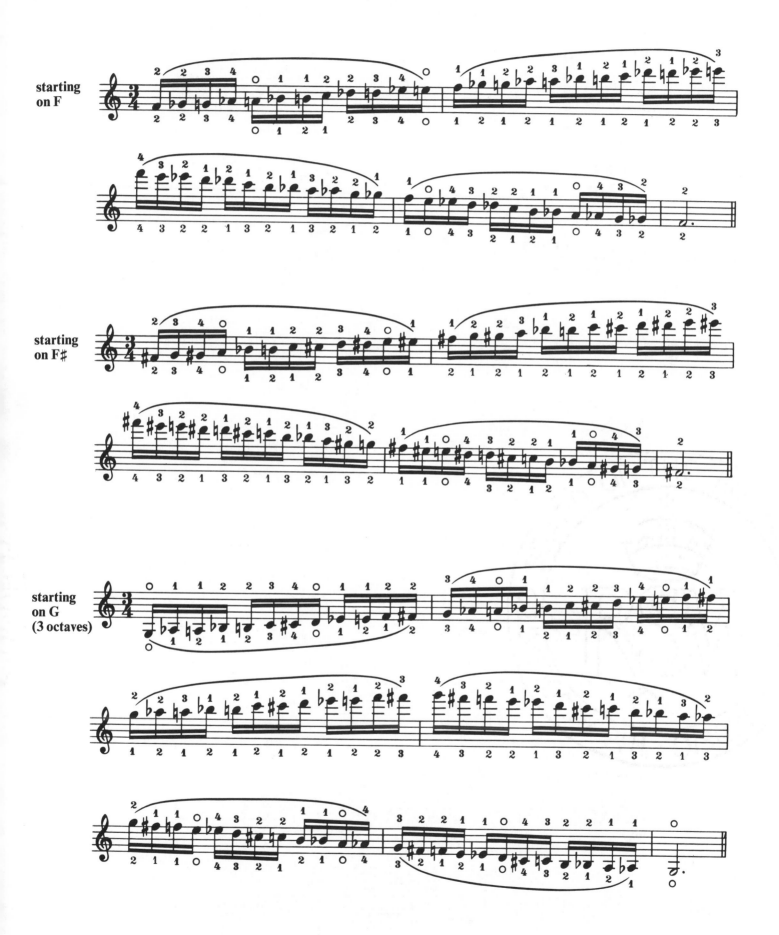

ARPEGGIOS: 2 octaves (Grades 6 & 8)

(a) separate bows, even notes; (b) slurred as shown, six notes to a bow

ARPEGGIOS: 3 octaves (Grades 6, 7 & 8)

(a) separate bows, even notes; (b) slurred as shown, three notes to a bow (Grade 6);
(c) slurred as shown, three *or* nine notes to a bow at candidate's choice (Grades 7 & 8)

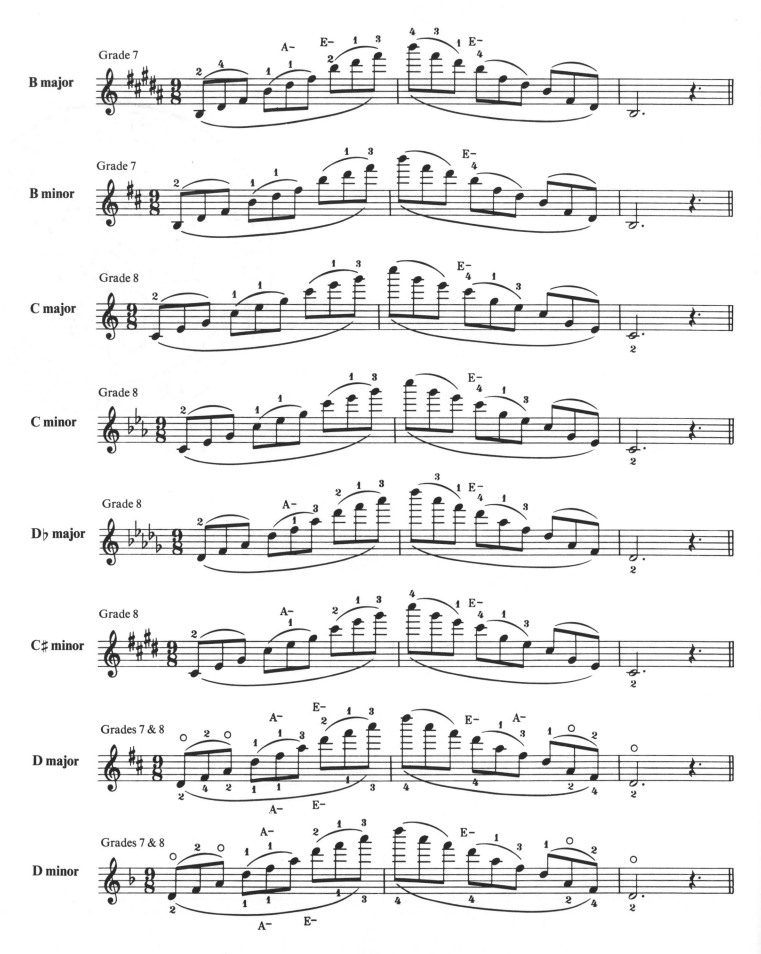

DOMINANT SEVENTHS: 2 octaves (Grades 6 & 7)

(a) separate bows, even notes; (b) slurred as shown, four notes to a bow (Grade 6);
(c) slurred as shown, four *or* eight notes to a bow at candidate's choice (Grade 7)

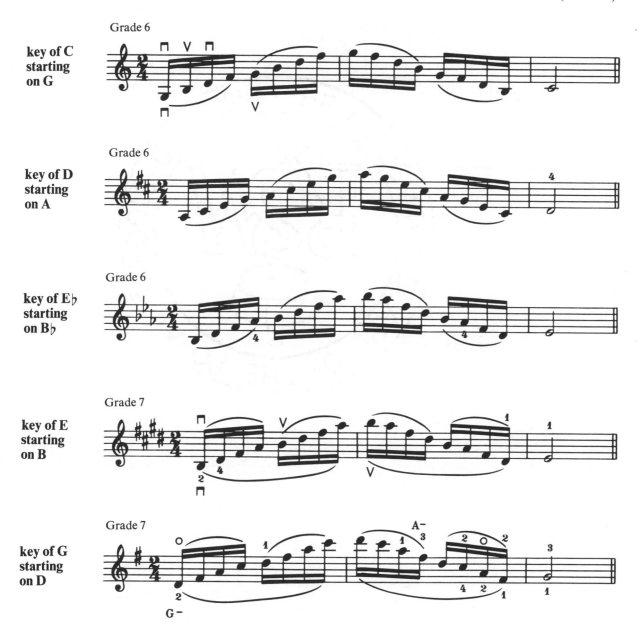

DOMINANT SEVENTHS: 3 octaves (Grades 7 & 8)

(a) separate bows, even notes; (b) slurred as shown, four *or* eight notes to a bow at candidate's choice (Grade 7);
(c) slurred as shown, four *or* twelve notes to a bow at candidate's choice (Grade 8)

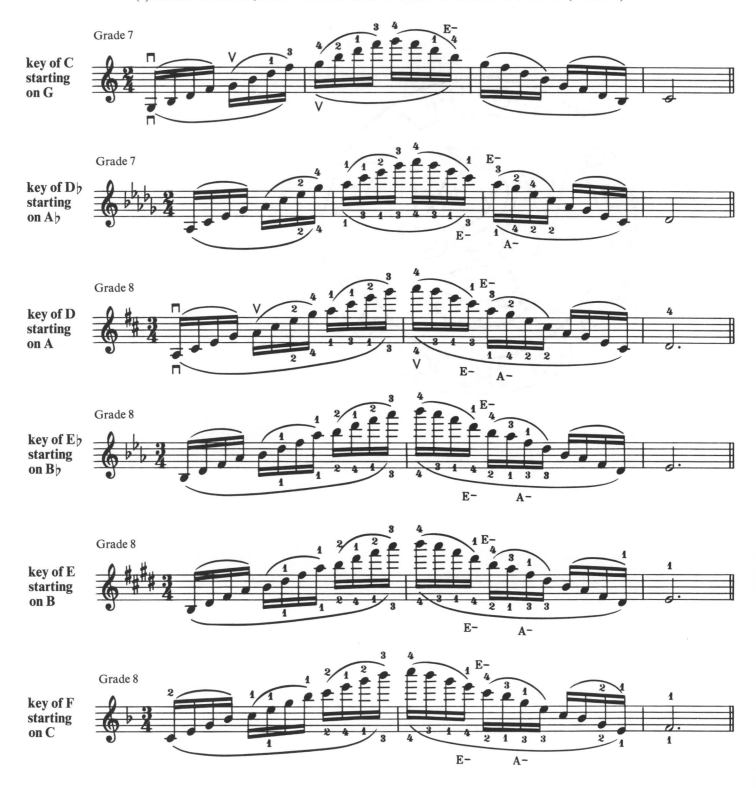

DIMINISHED SEVENTHS: 2 & 3 octaves (Grades 6, 7 & 8)

(a) separate bows, even notes; (b) slurred as shown, four notes to a bow (Grade 6);
(c) slurred as shown, four *or* eight notes to a bow at candidate's choice (Grade 7);
(d) slurred as shown, four *or* twelve notes to a bow at candidate's choice (Grade 8)

Grade 6
starting on G

Grades 6 & 7
starting on A

Grade 7
starting on A♭

Grade 7
starting on G

Grade 8
starting on A♭

Grade 8
starting on A

Grade 8
starting on B♭

In diminished sevenths, the notes have been written out harmonically but,
for the purpose of practical fingering, they do not always accord with theoretic notation.

DOUBLE STOP SCALES (Grades 6 & 7)

DOUBLE STOP SCALES (Grade 8)

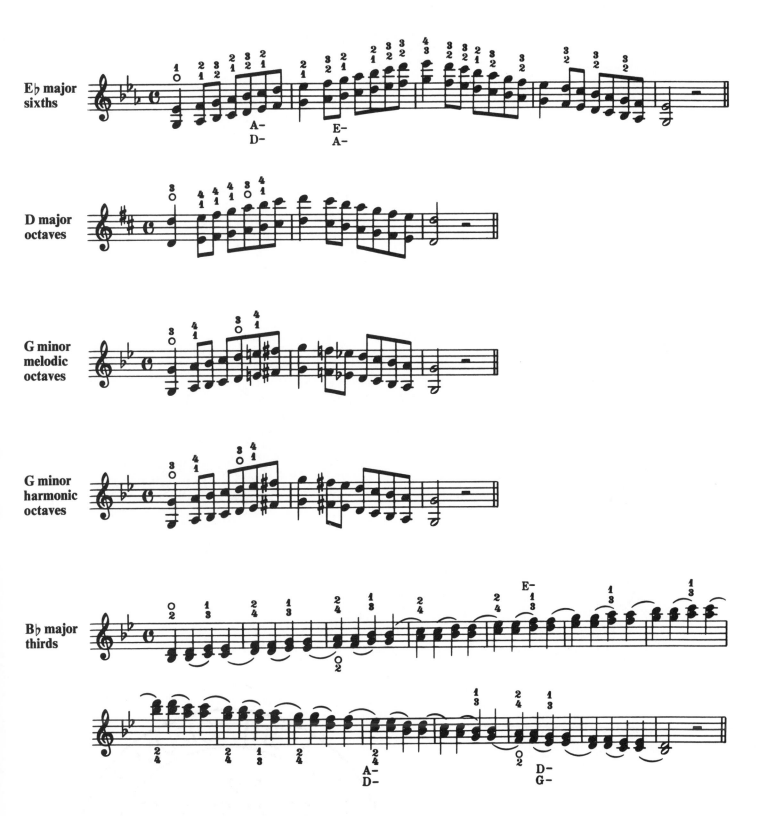